PROBLEM SOLVING WORKBOOK for Clever Kids®

Written by Kirstin Swanson

Illustrations and cover artwork by Chris Dickason

Edited by Frances Evans
Cover design by Angie Allison
Designed by Zoe Bradley

BUSTER BOOKS

HOW THIS BOOK WORKS

Maurice, Molly, Mo and Mia are four monsters who love maths. Can you use your problem-solving and reasoning skills to help the monsters complete the activities in this book?

Before you start, find a quiet place to work, away from any distractions. You can work through the book at your own pace and tackle the activities in any order you like.

The book is split into 12 sections, and each one focuses on a different maths topic. In each section, you'll find lots of activities that will help you to practise your problem-solving and reasoning skills. If you're finding a question difficult, talking it through with an adult might help. If you're still finding it tricky, move on to another question and come back to it another time. Once you've finished a section, give yourself a tick!

You'll also find some 'Top Tips' throughout the book, which give you hints to help you with the questions.

When you're finished, you can turn to page 54 to check your answers. You'll also find a glossary at the back, which explains key maths terms used in the book.

Good luck, and have fun!

CONTENTS

NUMBER AND PLACE VALUE

Use your knowledge of number and place value to answer these questions.

1) Can you use all three of these digit cards to answer the following questions?

a) What is the smallest 3-digit number you can make? ....

b) What is the largest 3-digit number you can make? ....

c) The 0 number card can only be used in the ones or the tens column when writing a 3-digit number – true or false? ....

2) Maurice is counting in fours. He starts at 20.

"20, 24, 28, 34, 38 ..."

Explain where Maurice has made a mistake.

....

....

3) Can you split the numbers below each monster into hundreds, tens and ones? An answer has been added for you to show you how it works.

458

807

361

4) Molly is making numbers with different items. She has decided to use buttons for ones, unicorn horns for tens and moon rocks for hundreds.

a) What numbers has she made?

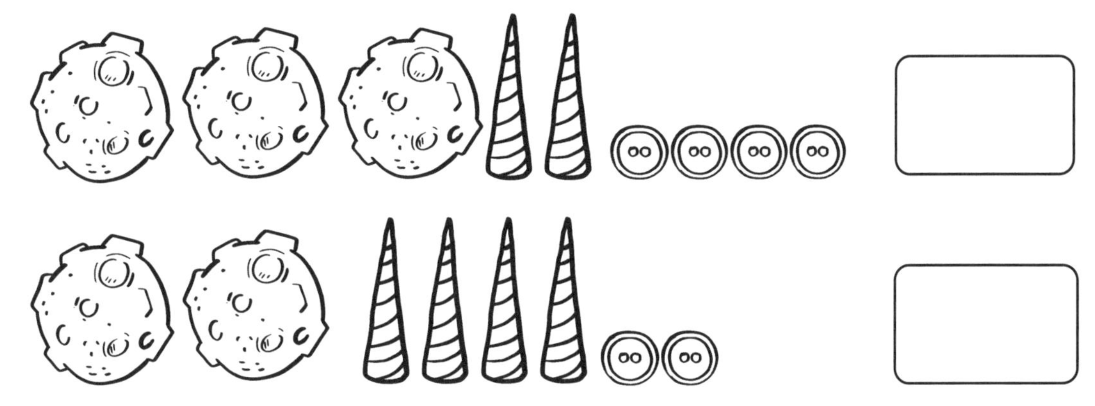

b) Can you use moon rocks, unicorn horns and buttons to draw the number 135 in this space?

5) Molly has built a function machine. Any number she puts in, the machine will add 10 to it.

a) What would the next number be if Molly put 192 into the machine?

....

b) Maurice says that if he puts 112 into the machine, the next number would be 120. Is he correct? Explain your answer.

....

....

....

TOP TIP!

When working with large numbers, try writing the first letter (or letters) of each digit's place value above it, to help you identify the number. Use 'Th' for thousands, 'H' for hundreds, 'T' for tens and 'O' for ones. For example:

Th	H	T	O
6	5	7	2

NUMBER AND PLACE VALUE CONTINUED

You're doing great! Now, try these questions.

1) Each of these monsters has 6 eyes.

a) Altogether, how many eyes are there on the 5 monsters? ....

b) Mo says that if there were 12 monsters, there would be 66 eyes. Do you agree?

Yes / No

Explain why.

....

....

2) Maurice and Molly are playing a game. Maurice thinks of a number and Molly has to guess it. Maurice gives these clues:

It has 1 thousand.

It has 2 ones.

The hundreds digit is double the ones digit.

The tens digit is less than 5.

What could the number be? Write all the possible answers in the boxes on the right.

3) **Molly and Maurice are rounding numbers to the nearest 100. They are talking about the number 235.**

Maurice says:

The number will round up to 300 because it has a 5 in it.

Molly says:

The number will round down because we need to look at the tens digit.

Who do you agree with? Explain why.

....

....

4) **Molly is counting backwards in steps of 1000. She starts on the number 6202.**

What are the next four numbers?

....

5) **Maurice says that after 10,202, the next number when counting forwards in steps of 1000 is 20,202.**

What mistake has he made? Explain your reasoning.

....

....

HOORAY, FINISHED! ☐

ADDITION AND SUBTRACTION

Use your addition and subtraction skills to answer these questions.

1) Can you solve the calculations?

a)

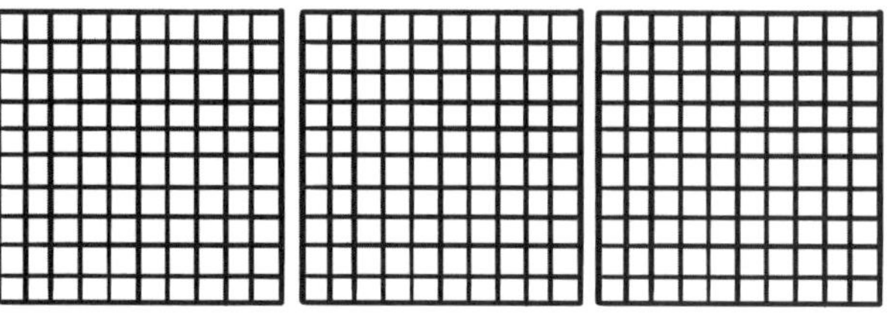

+ 9 = ☐

b)

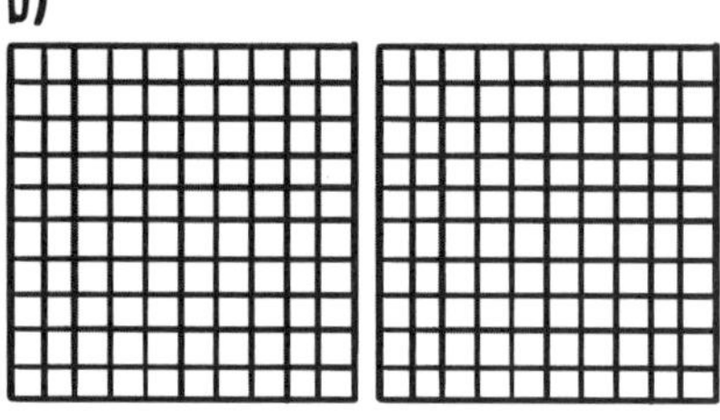

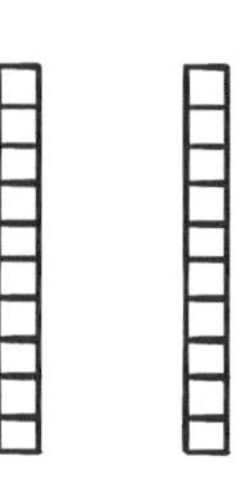

- 20 = ☐

2) Mo is practising his addition.

Can you help him figure out what the missing numbers are?

```
   2 1 5        ☐ 5 8        ☐ 9 6
 + 1 ☐ 3      + 3 3 ☐      + 4 ☐ 4
 -------      -------      -------
   ☐ 5 ☐        7 ☐ 7      1 0 2 ☐
```

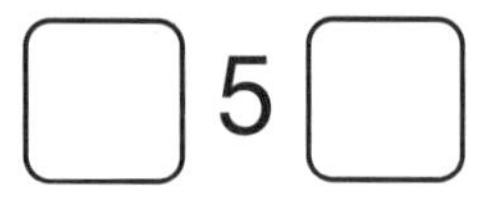

3) Here is a subtraction that Maurice has completed.

```
  586        586
- 347      - 347
  ---        ---
  241
```

What mistake has he made? Can you calculate the correct answer?

....

....

....

4) Complete these bar models to find the missing part or whole.

....

....

746	
432	

328	595

5) Can you rearrange the numbers to write the addition and subtraction fact families for the different monster mansions? Some answers have been added to help you.

a) 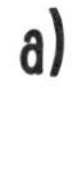

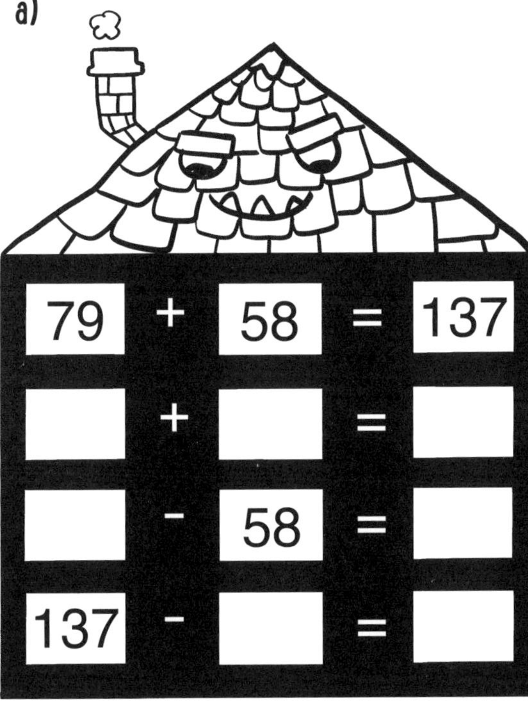

b)

TOP TIP!

Using the 'inverse operation' (the opposite) is a great way to solve missing number problems and to check your work. For example, once you have completed a subtraction, add the two smaller numbers together. If the answer is the remaining number, you know your calculation is correct.

ADDITION AND SUBTRACTION CONTINUED

You're doing great! Now, try these questions.

1) Molly says:

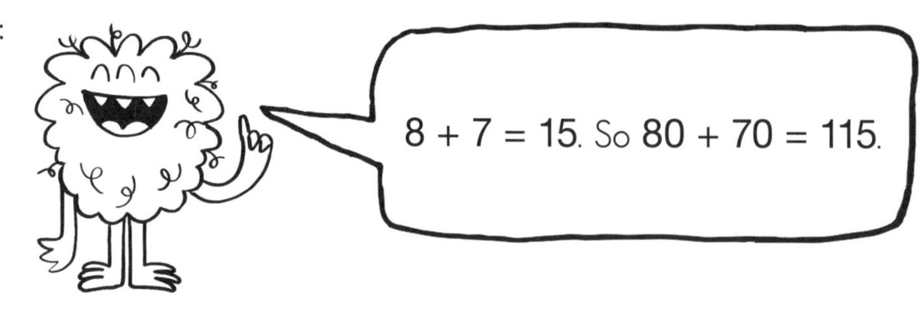

Do you agree? Yes / No

Explain your reasoning.

....

....

2) Complete the sentences:

If I know that 60 + 40 = 100 then 600 + 400 = ☐

If I know that 200 - 130 = 70 then 2000 - ☐ = 700

3) Maurice has completed a written subtraction.

$$\begin{array}{r} 5472 \\ -\,2381 \\ \hline 3111 \end{array}$$

Can you spot his mistake? Rewrite the calculation correctly here.

4) Mia and Mo are having a go at estimating. They're trying to estimate the answer to 6943 – 2037.

Mia says:

I think the answer will be around **4000** because 6000 - 2000 = 4000

Mo says:

I think the answer will be around **5000** because 7000 - 2000 = 5000

Whose answer is more realistic? Why?

....

....

5) 1200 monsters are looking at their similarities and differences. 734 are hairy, 329 have horns and the rest are covered in scales.

How many monsters have scales?

....

HOORAY, FINISHED! ☐

MULTIPLICATION AND DIVISION

Use your multiplication and division skills to answer these questions.

1) The monsters are organizing some party food.

a) Can you write the multiplication facts for each array?

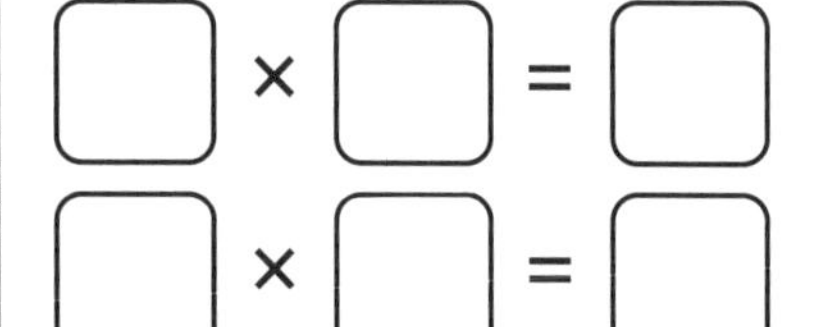

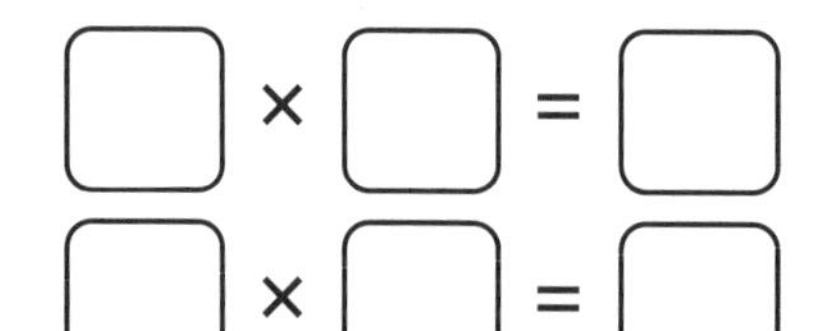

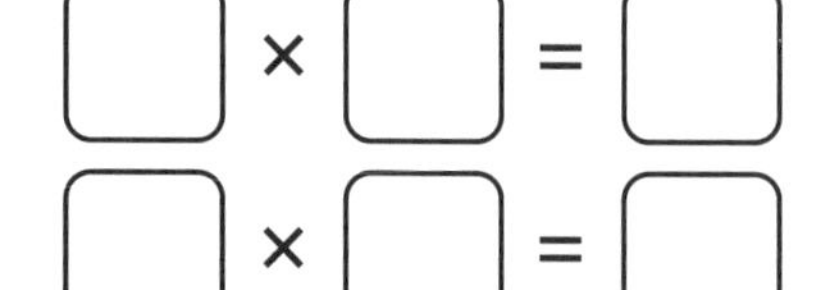

b) Show how you could calculate how much party food there is altogether.

....

2) 7 monsters have been invited to the party and each one has 3 heads.

How many party hats will they need altogether?

....

....

3) 24 cups have been ordered for the party. Maurice thinks they should be put on the table in one long line of 24 cups. Molly thinks there are lots of other ways to organize the cups neatly as an array.

How could the 24 cups be organized into different arrays?
Draw the different solutions in the space below.

4) When some of the monsters have a birthday, they have a growth spurt!

How much taller would these monsters be if they grew:

64 cm

3 × taller?

....

31 cm

4 × taller?

....

23 cm

8 × taller?

....

5) Mo says that the first monster has grown the most because it is now the tallest.

Is Mo correct? Explain your reasoning.

....

....

TOP TIP!

Multiplication (and addition) is 'commutative'. This means that when multiplying two numbers together, you can swap their position in the number sentence and still get the same value. For example, $2 \times 5 = 10$ and $5 \times 2 = 10$.

MULTIPLICATION AND DIVISION CONTINUED

Now, have a go at these questions.

1) Maurice knows that 4 × 6 = 24.

Use this knowledge to complete the following calculations.

240 ÷ 6 = ☐ 40 × ☐ = 2400 24,000 ÷ 6 = ☐

2) Molly says:

Is this always true, sometimes true, or never true?
What calculations can you use to support your answer?

....

....

3) Maurice says 5552 is a multiple of 5 because it has 3 fives in it.

Do you agree? Explain why.

....

....

....

4) Molly is thinking of 2 numbers. Their product is 48. One of the numbers is a 2-digit number, the other is a 1-digit number.

a) What numbers could Molly be thinking of?

....

....

b) Maurice says he can think of two 1-digit numbers which also multiply together to give 48. What are they?

....

....

5) Molly and Maurice have created multiplication sentences. Have they written these correctly?

Tick or cross their calculations and rewrite any errors.

$9 \times 4 = 2 \times 6 \times 3$ ☐ ....

$3 \times 2 \times 7 = 8 \times 6$ ☐ ....

$5 \times 12 = 5 \times 3 \times 2$ ☐ ....

HOORAY, FINISHED! ☐

FRACTIONS

Use your knowledge of fractions to answer these questions.

1) Molly is practising her knowledge of tenths.

a) Complete the number line by counting in tenths.

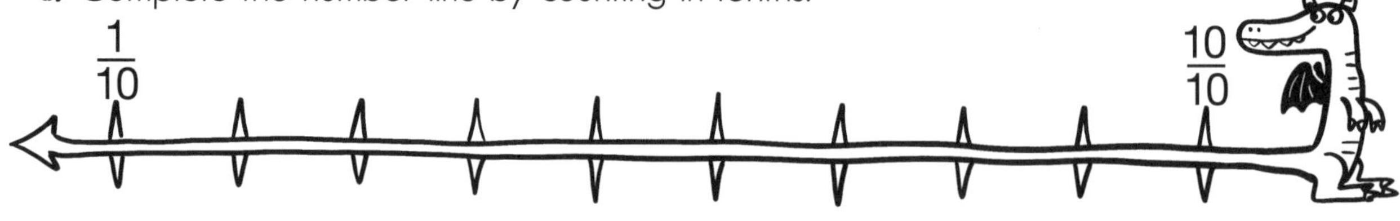

b) Molly says that when you write $\frac{5}{10}$ you could write $\frac{1}{2}$ instead.
Is she correct? Explain why.

2) Molly and Maurice are trying to work out how much pizza they have left.

Maurice has:

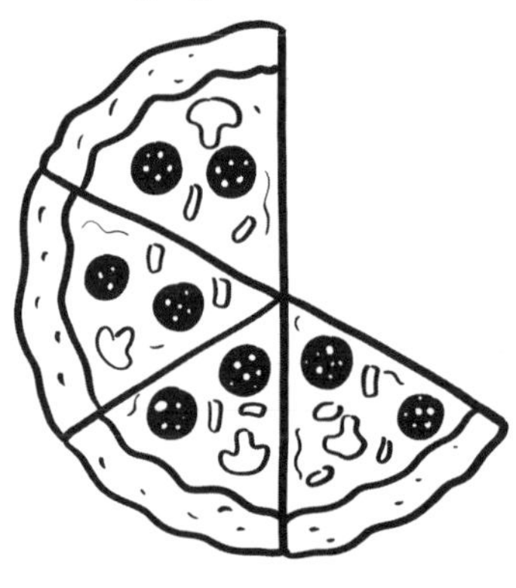

Molly has:

They think that, altogether, they have $\frac{7}{12}$ because $\frac{4}{6} + \frac{3}{6} = \frac{7}{12}$
Are they correct?

3) Is the following statement always true, sometimes true or never true?

When comparing fractions which both have a numerator of 1, the fraction with the larger denominator is always greater.

4) **Write the fractions for the following:**

a) How many of this monster's spots are grey?

b) How many of this monster's eyes are open?

c) How many of this monster's heads have horns?

5) **Can you show $\frac{1}{4}$ on each of these shapes by shading in the squares?**

TOP TIP!

Drawing pictures or bar models can be really helpful when trying to solve fraction problems.

FRACTIONS CONTINUED

You're doing great! Now, have a go at these questions.

1) Molly and Maurice are eating some cheesecakes.

Molly has eaten $\frac{6}{9}$ of her cheesecake.

Maurice has eaten $\frac{5}{9}$ of his.

How much have they eaten altogether?

$\frac{\square}{\square}$

2) Take a look at these groups of monsters and answer the following questions.

a) What fraction of these monsters have wings?

$\frac{\square}{\square}$

b) What fraction of these monsters have black horns?

$\frac{\square}{\square}$

c) What fraction of these monsters have spots?

$\frac{\square}{\square}$

3) Using the digit cards, what equivalent fractions could you make?

4	8	15	2	3	20	1

....

....

4) Solve these fraction subtractions:

a) $\frac{9}{10} - \frac{4}{10} = \frac{\square}{\square}$

b) $\frac{8}{10} - \frac{1}{10} = \frac{9}{10} - \frac{\square}{10}$

c) 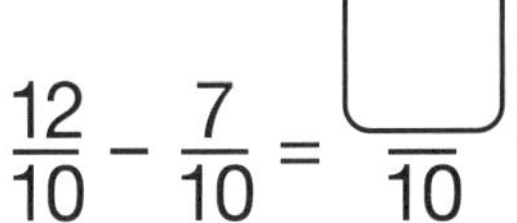

$\frac{12}{10} - \frac{7}{10} = \frac{\square}{10}$ which is equivalent to $\frac{\square}{2}$

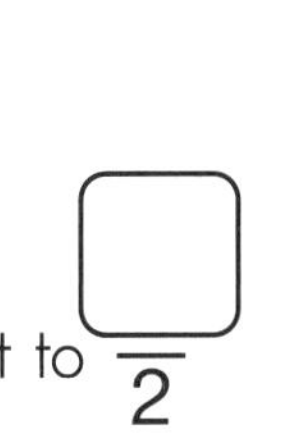

5) Molly says:

$\frac{3}{8} + \frac{5}{8} = 1$ whole

Draw pictures in the space below to show that she is correct.

HOORAY, FINISHED! ☐

LENGTH

Can you use your knowledge of length to answer these questions?

1) The monsters are measuring their shadows.

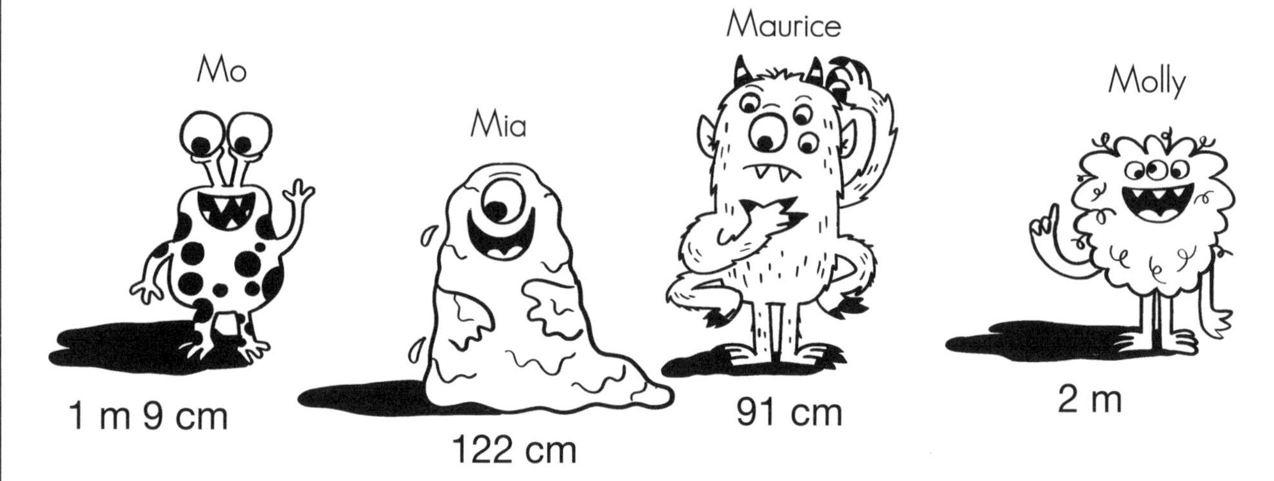

a) Who has the longest shadow? ....

b) Who has the shortest shadow? ....

c) What is the difference between the longest and shortest shadow?

....

2) How long is this monster's tail?

a) .... centimetres.

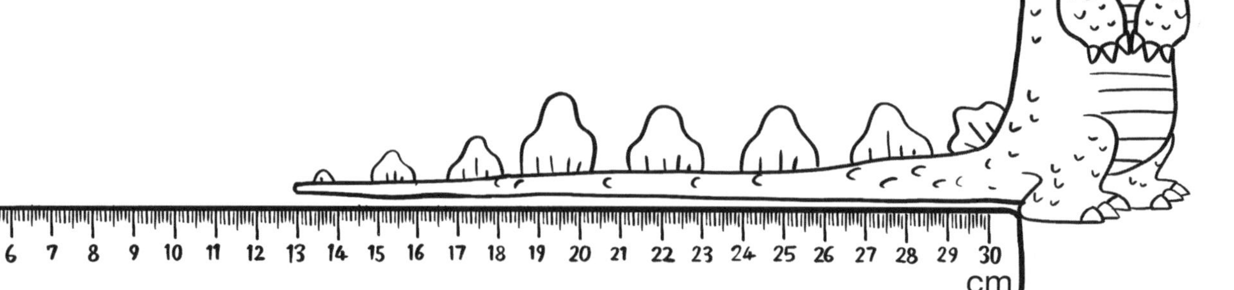

b) What would the measurement be in millimetres? ....

3) Match the measurements on the left with their equivalent measurement on the right.

45 mm	450 cm
4 m 50 cm	45 cm
450 mm	4.5 cm

4) Maurice can jump 30 cm into the air. Molly can jump 5 times as high.

How high can Molly jump?

....

5) Molly has a collection of shapes:

She wants to calculate the perimeter of each of them. She says:

I can find the length of one side and multiply that by the number of sides.

Is Molly correct? Explain why.

....

....

TOP TIP!

If possible, try to estimate your answer first when measuring or calculating length. That way, you can consider if your answer is realistic.

LENGTH CONTINUED

You're doing great! Now, have a go at these questions.

1) Convince the monsters that 300 metres is less than 3 kilometres.

....

....

....

....

2) Is the following statement always true, sometimes true or never true?

When converting from mm to cm, you multiply by 10.

....

....

3) These shapes are not drawn to scale. Can you calculate the perimeter of the shapes using the measurements given?

a)

2 cm

3 cm

5 cm

4 cm

8 cm

....

b)

19 cm

6 cm

14 cm

3 cm

5 cm

....

4) **Maurice says that none of the shapes below can have the same area because they all look different.**

Is he correct?

....

....

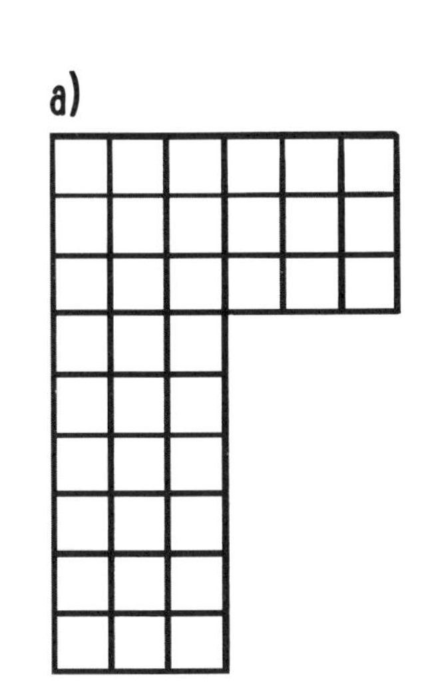

a)

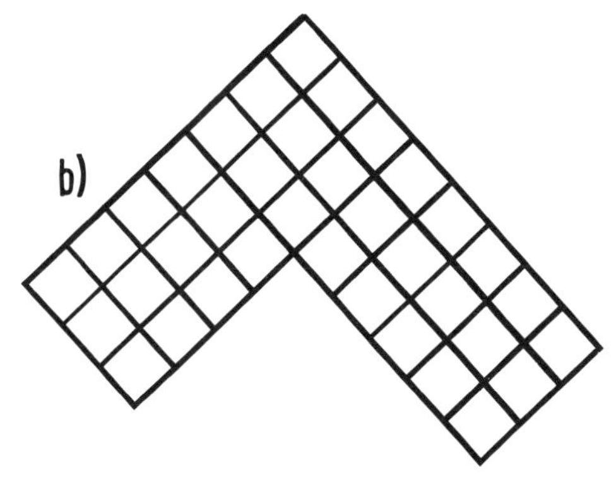

b)

c)

5) **If I know that 1000 m = 1 km then I also know that:**

a) 2000 m = ☐ km

b) 5 km = ☐ m

c) 3600 m = ☐ km and ☐ m

HOORAY, FINISHED! ☐

MASS AND CAPACITY

Can you use your knowledge of mass and capacity to answer these questions?

1) Which monster is the heaviest?

....

a)

0 kg
30 kg
10 kg
20 kg

b)

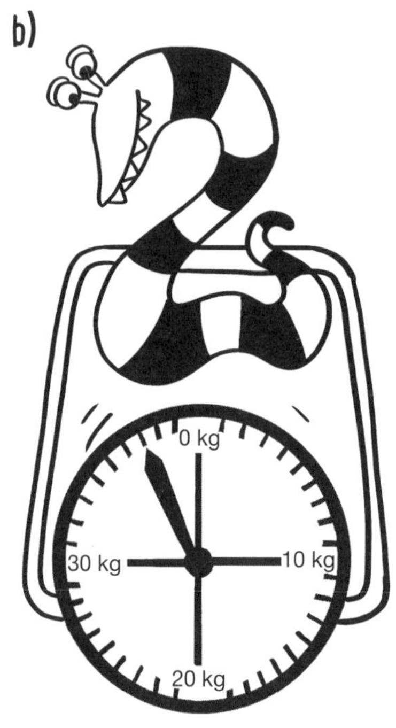

c)

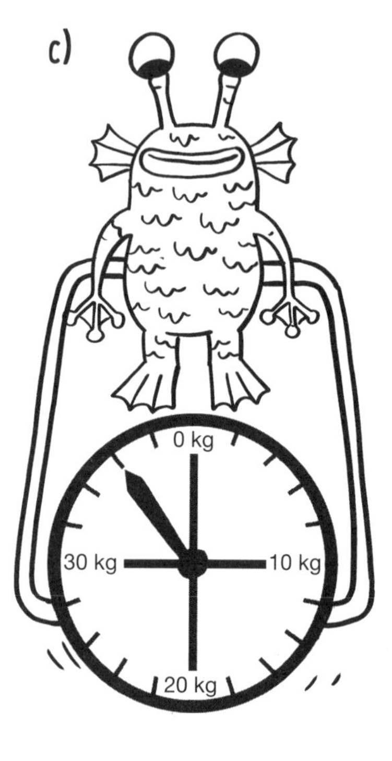

2) Molly and Maurice are sharing a 1-litre jug of squash. Molly drinks 200 millilitres. Maurice drinks 125 millilitres.

How much squash is left?

....

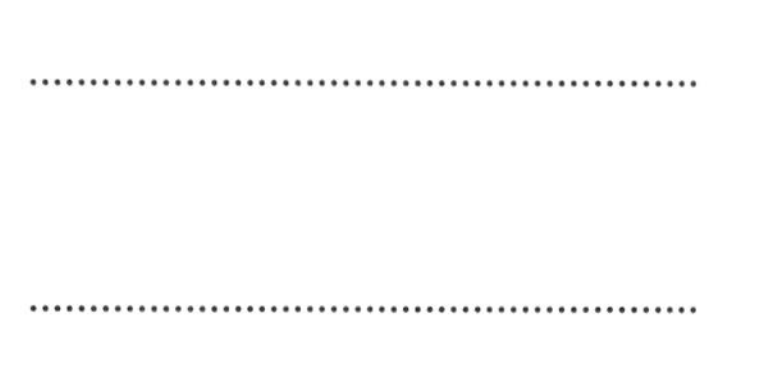

....

3) Maurice says that $\frac{3}{4}$ of a kilogram is 340 grams.

Is he correct?

....

4) **The monsters are making a cake which serves 4 monsters.**

Can you adjust the recipe so that it would serve 2 monsters and 8 monsters?

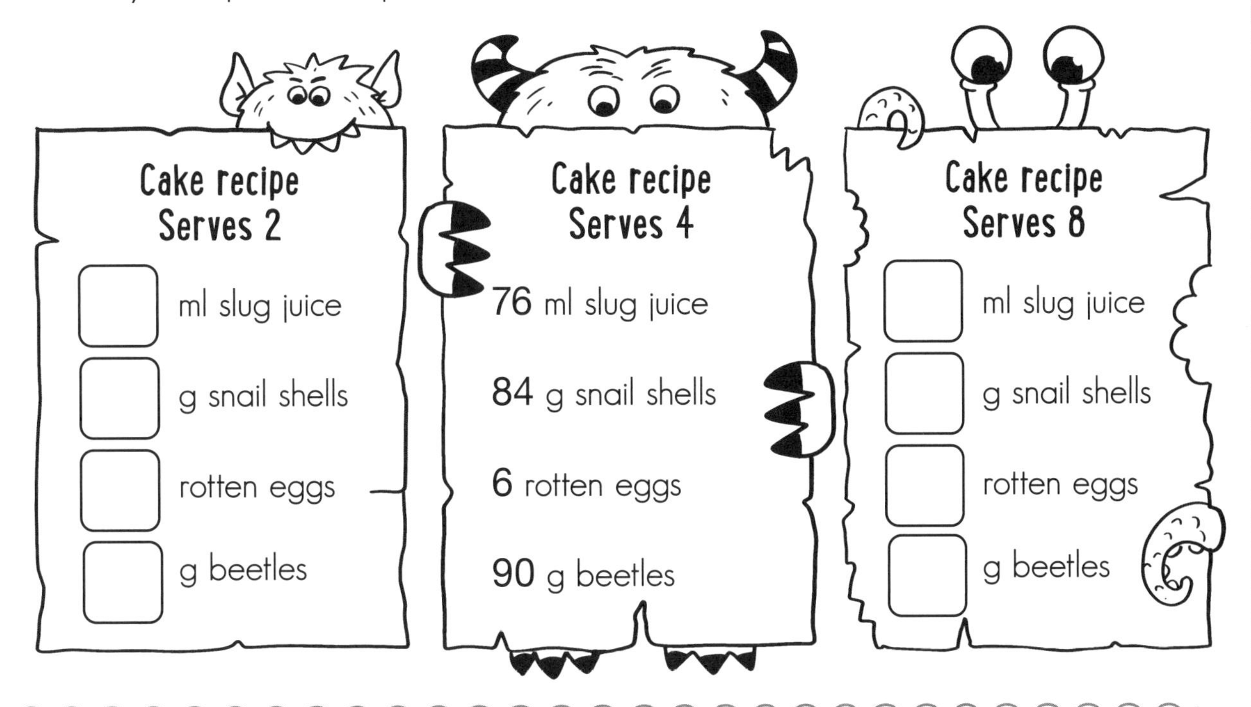

5) **The monsters have been pouring water into 1-litre jugs which only have some measurements marked on them.**

Can you work out how much water is in each jug?

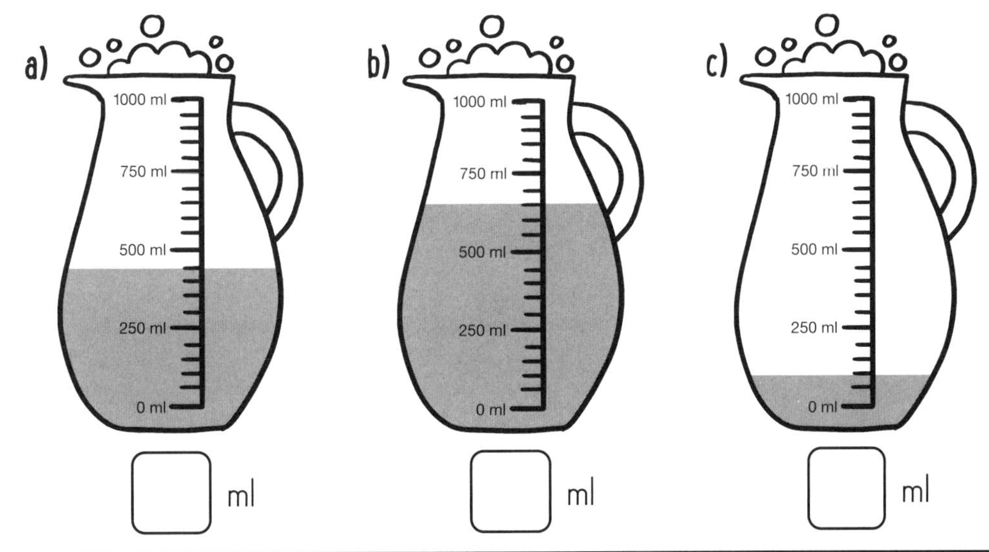

TOP TIP!

When converting between grams (g) and kilograms (kg) and between millilitres (ml) and litres (L) you will always be using the number 1000.

MASS AND CAPACITY CONTINUED

You're doing great! Now, have a go at these questions.

1) Put these items in order from largest to smallest based on how much liquid they could hold.

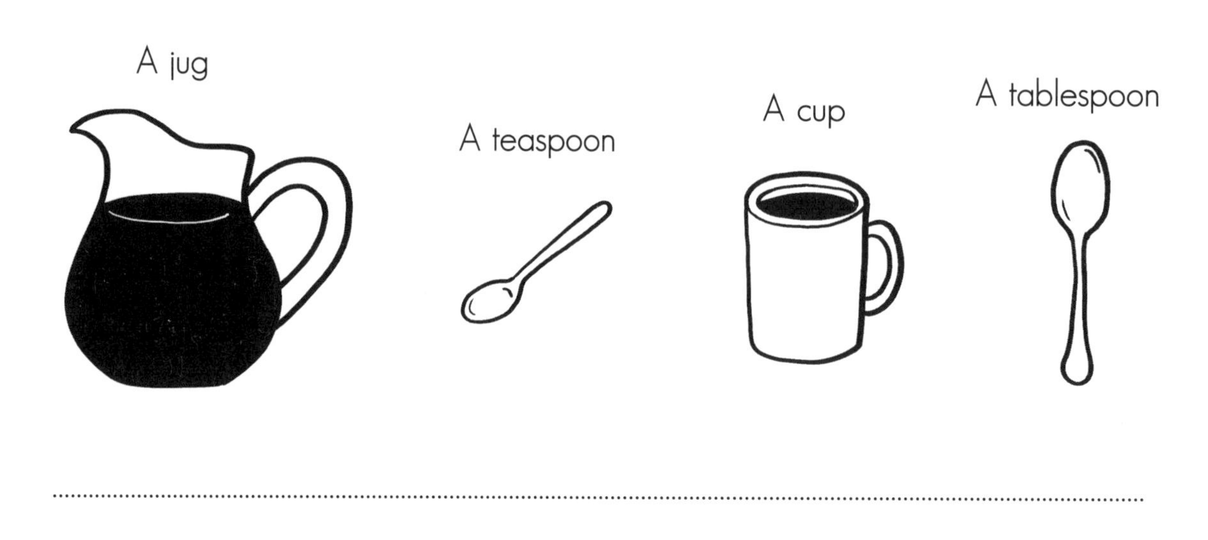

....

2) Two identical adult monsters are stood on one side of a weighing scale. Eight mini monsters are stood on the other side. One mini monster weighs 4 kg. The scales are balanced.

How much does one adult monster weigh?

....

....

3) Molly has a bottle that holds 550 ml. Maurice has a bottle that holds 3 times this amount.

How much liquid can Maurice's bottle hold?

Write your answer in ml: ☐ ml

4) Use greater than, less than or equals symbols to make these statements correct:

5 kg and 600 g ☐ 560 g

1L and 750 ml ☐ 1750 ml

958 g ☐ 9 kg and 580 g

5) Draw lines to match the following items with the unit you would normally use to measure them.

L

g

kg

ml

HOORAY, FINISHED! ☐

MONEY

Can you use your knowledge of money to answer these questions?

1) Mia has 80p in total in silver coins. In one hand, she has a 50p coin.

What coins could she have in the other hand?

Write all the possibilities.

2) Molly and Maurice are comparing the amount of pocket money they have.

Molly has a £5 note, three 20ps and two 5ps.

Maurice has 6 pound coins, a 10p, two 2ps and 1p.

Molly says she has more money because she has a note.

Is she correct?

....

3) Complete these bar models:

£4 and 50p	
85p	

£1 and 14p	99p

4) **Maurice has £5 and he wants to buy two items from the joke shop.**

Which two items could he buy? Write down all the combinations.

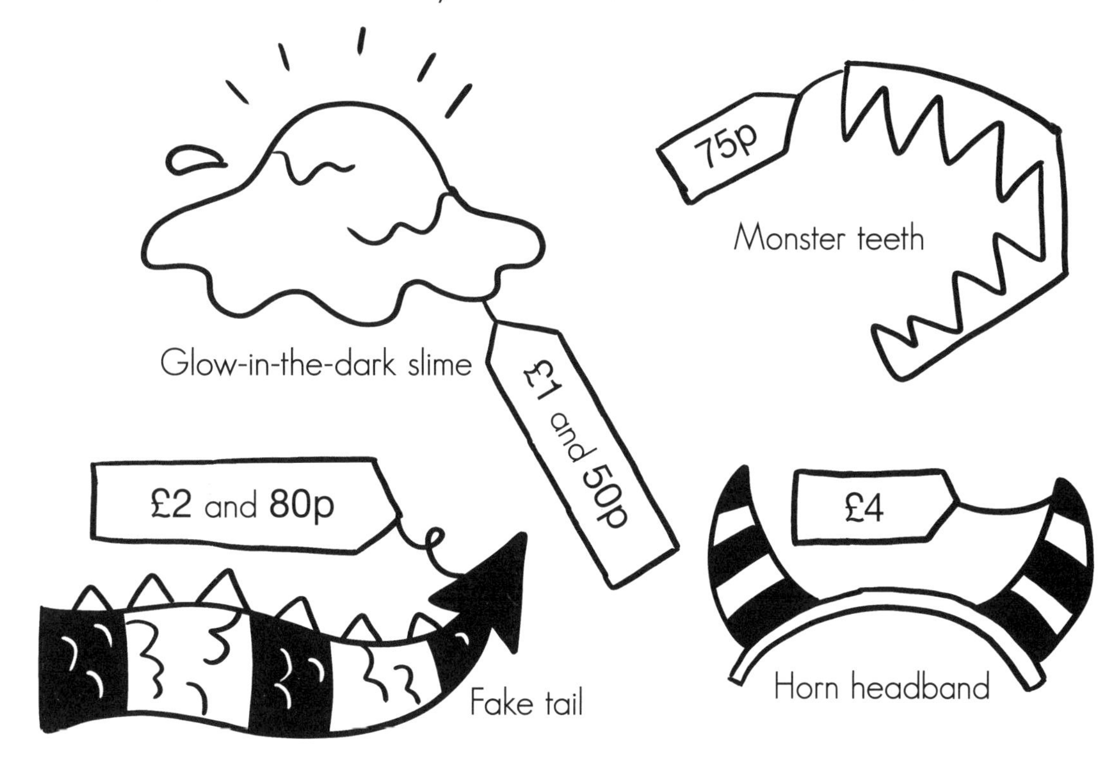

....

....

5) **True or False: you need five 50ps to make £5.**

....

TOP TIP!

When you're trying to calculate an amount of money in your head, it can be easier to work out the larger notes and coins first, and then work out the smaller ones.

MONEY CONTINUED

You're doing great! Now, have a go at these questions.

1) Maurice has the following amount of money in his monster bank:

A £10 note, a £2 coin, a £1 coin, two 20p coins and a 2p coin.

Maurice says you can write this as £13.42. Is he correct?

....

2) Here are some digit cards.

What amounts can you make that are greater than £7.00 and less than £9.00? For example, £7.01.

7	8	0	1

....

....

....

3) Mia goes to the joke shop and buys a pop-up snake for £6 and a spooky spider for 45p. She pays with a £10 note.

How much change does she get?

....

....

4) Molly has saved up £42. She spends $\frac{1}{6}$ of it. How much money does she have left?

Use the bar model to help you.

£7					

5) Mia and Mo both have £1 in total to spend at the sweetshop.

Mia has 2 coins. Mo has 4 coins. Between them, they have three 50p coins. What coins do they each have?

....

HOORAY, FINISHED! ☐

TELLING THE TIME

Can you use your knowledge of time to answer these questions?

1) These clocks show what times the monsters go to bed.

Write the time in words under each clock.

Molly

Mia

Mo

a) ....

b) Which monster goes to bed the earliest?

....

2) The monsters have been racing through their house to see who can run from the basement to the attic door the quickest. Molly took 17 seconds. Mo took 15 seconds.

Molly says:

I was quicker because 17 is greater than 15.

Is she correct? Explain why.

....

....

3) Put these times in order from shortest to longest:

Half an hour   60 minutes   60 seconds   15 seconds

....

4) Read the time on these clocks to the nearest minute.

a) .... b) .... c) ....

5) Explain how to work out how many hours there are in 180 minutes.

....

....

....

TOP TIP!

Remember, on an analogue clock, you use the long hand to read the minutes and the short hand to read the hour.

TELLING THE TIME CONTINUED

You're doing great! Now, have a go at these questions.

1) Draw lines to match the analogue times to the digital times.

2) Molly is going to a swimming lesson. The lesson starts at 15:00. It takes her 35 minutes to walk to the swimming pool and she needs 5 minutes to get changed.

What time does she need to leave her house?

....

3) Molly takes 32 seconds to swim one length of the pool.

How long would it take her to swim 5 lengths? Write your answer in seconds.

....

4) Mo has stayed up far too late and the time on his 24-hour clock reads 23:54. It takes him 8 minutes to brush his teeth.

What time will his clock read when he has finished brushing his teeth?

....

5) Mia is practising reading and writing the time. Here is an analogue clock. She has written that the time is quarter to 10.

What mistake has she made?

....

....

....

12 1 2 3 4 5 6 7 8 9 10 11

HOORAY, FINISHED! ☐

TIME AND DATES

Can you use your knowledge of dates and time to answer these questions?

1) Use greater than, less than or equals symbols to make these statements correct:

1 minute ☐ 100 seconds

Number of days in January ☐ Number of days in February

30 days ☐ Number of days in September

2) Mo thinks that knowing the 6 times table can help him when he needs to convert minutes into hours. He says:

If I know that $12 \div 6 = 2$ I can use that to help me calculate that 120 minutes ÷ 60 minutes is 2. That means that 120 minutes is equal to 2 hours.

Do you agree? Can you give another example using a multiple of 6?

....

....

....

3) The monsters are confused by how many ways humans talk about time.

Can you complete the sentences using the words provided?

morning afternoon midnight

midday noon

12 o'clock in the afternoon is also known as .... or ....

00:00 on a digital clock is also known as ....

4:30 am would be 4:30 in the ....

4:30 pm would be 4:30 in the ....

4) Which months of the year have 30 days or less?

....

....

5) Some of the monsters sleep for longer during the winter.

Put a tick next to the monster who sleeps the most per day.

Molly sleeps for half a day.

Mo sleeps from 7:45 pm to 9:00 am.

Maurice sleeps for 14 hours.

TOP TIP!

To show a 24-hour time in the afternoon (or when it has pm after it), you can add 12 to the number of hours. For example: 4:25 pm would be 16:25 because 4 + 12 = 16.

TIME AND DATES CONTINUED

You're doing great! Now, have a go at these questions.

Different countries often have different 'time zones', depending on where they are in the world. For example, when it's 2:00 pm in Britain it will be 3:00 pm in France, or it might be 2:00 am in New Zealand. The exact differences between countries can vary, depending on the seasons.

1) French time is 1 hour ahead of British time.

If it's **8:00** am in Britain, then what time is it in France? ....

2) When it's midnight in New York City, on the east coast of the United States, it's 9:00 pm in Los Angeles, on the west coast.

So if it is now midday in Los Angeles, what time is it in New York City?

....

3) Maurice is going to the airport to head off on his summer holidays. He is flying from Britain to Italy. Italy is 1 hour ahead of British time.

a) Maurice's flight leaves at 16:45 British time. He needs to check in 2 hours before that time.

What time does Maurice need to check in? Write your answer in 24-hour time.

....

b) Maurice's flight lasts for 1 hour and 35 minutes.

What time will his flight land in Italy? Remember, Italy is 1 hour ahead of British time. Write your answer in 24-hour time.

....

c) It will take Maurice 25 minutes to get from the airport to his hotel.

At what time will he reach the hotel? Write your answer in 24-hour time.

....

HOORAY, FINISHED! ☐

GEOMETRY

Can you use your knowledge of geometry to answer these questions?

1) **Draw lines to match the monsters' stripes to the correct descriptions.**

perpendicular lines　　　vertical　　　horizontal

2) **The monsters have been sharpening their claws against these different tree trunks.**

Which of the claw marks are NOT parallel lines and why?

....

....

3) Put these shapes in order from most to least amount of internal right angles:

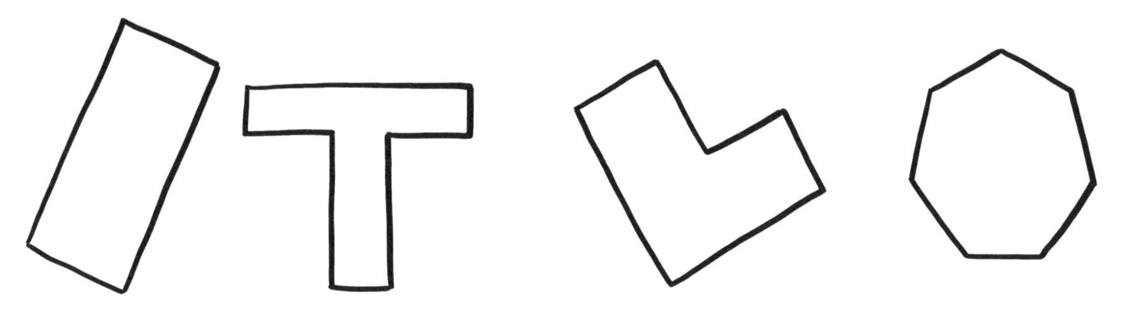

4) The monsters are playing 'Guess my Shape'.

Molly says that the shape she is thinking of is a 3D shape.

It has 5 vertices.

It has 8 edges.

It has 5 faces.

What shape is she thinking of?

....

5) Which of these nets would not make a cube?

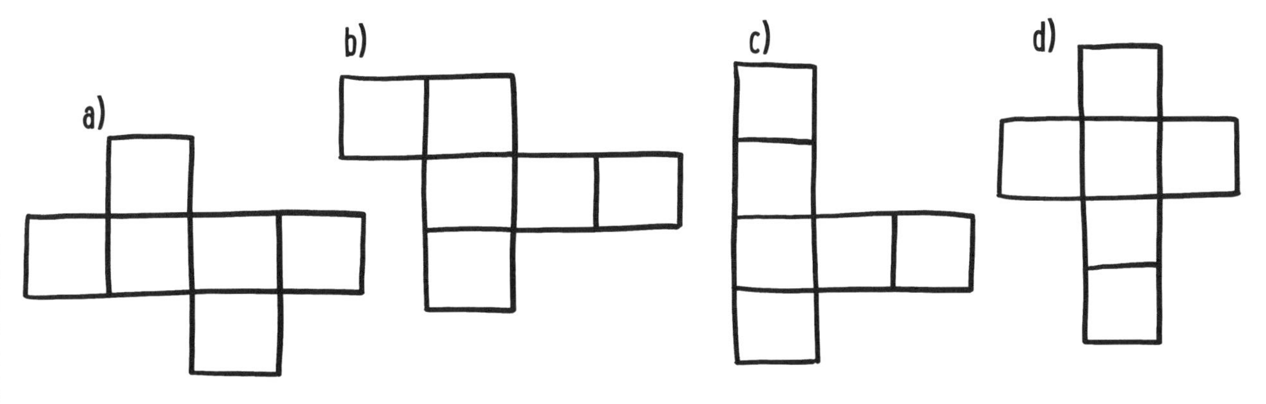

TOP TIP!

When answering questions about shapes, try to sketch out possible answers to help you. This may be easier than trying to think of lots of different shapes in your head at once.

GEOMETRY CONTINUED

You're doing great! Now, have a go at these questions.

1) Maurice is attempting to draw triangles. Are all the shapes he has drawn below triangles?

Yes / No

Explain your answer.

....

....

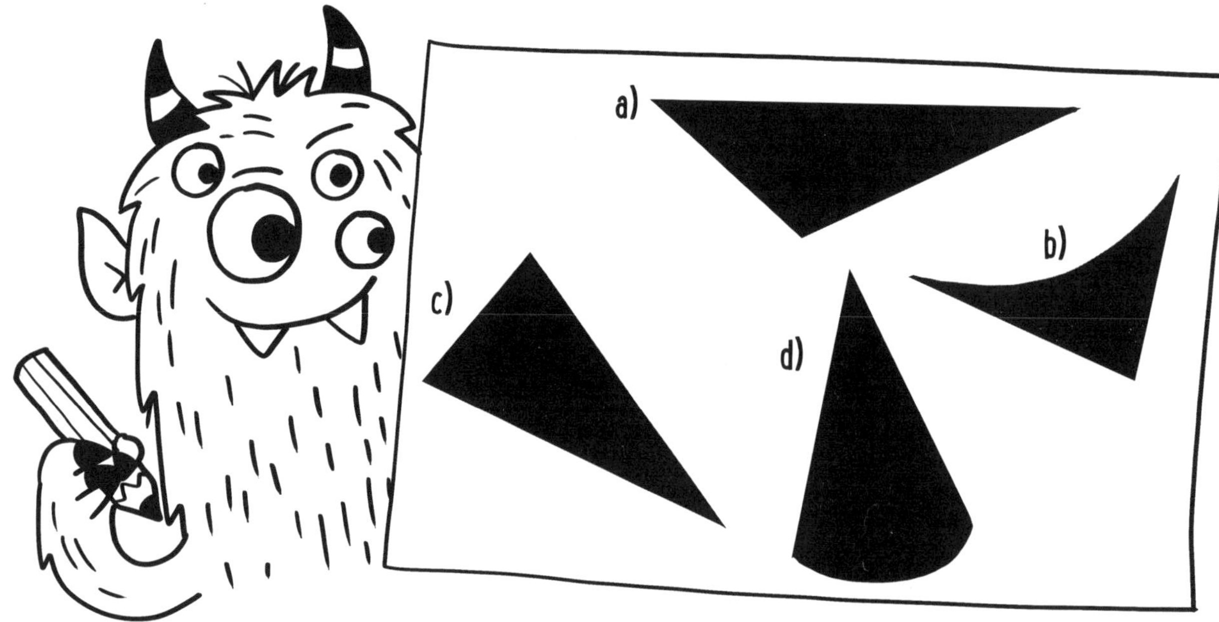

2) Is the following statement always true, sometimes true or never true?

Quadrilaterals have 2 sets of parallel lines.

Use the space below if you need to work out your answer.

....

3) Can you complete the symmetrical monsters on the other side of the mirror line?

4) Can you help the monsters to name these different types of angles?

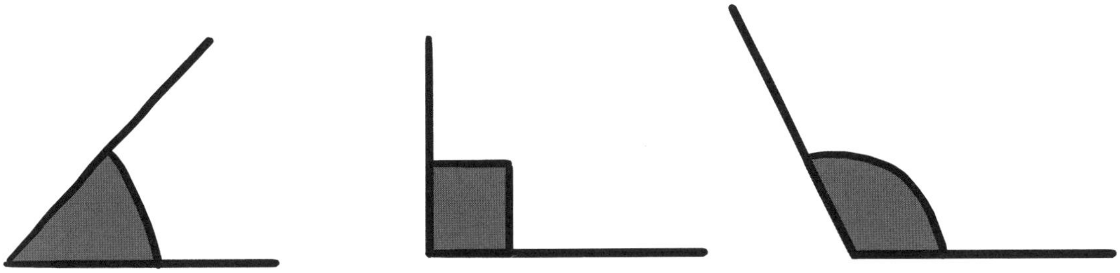

a) ....

b) ....

c) ....

5) Draw all the lines of symmetry on these monster cookies.

HOORAY, FINISHED! ☐

POSITION AND DIRECTION

Can you use your knowledge of position and direction to answer these questions?

1) The monsters are playing party games. They take it in turns to be blindfolded and spun round. When they've been spun round, they have to work out which way they are facing.

a) Molly starts off facing north. She is turned through 3 right angles anti-clockwise. Which way is she facing now?

....

b) Maurice starts off facing south. He is turned through 1 right angle anti-clockwise and then a half turn clockwise. Which way is he facing now?

....

2) Can you prove the following statement: A whole turn is equivalent to 4 quarter turns.

Use the space below if you need to work out your answer.

....

3) The monsters are packing for a trip but they are very messy and their belongings are all over the place.

Can you help the monsters find them using the coordinate grid below?

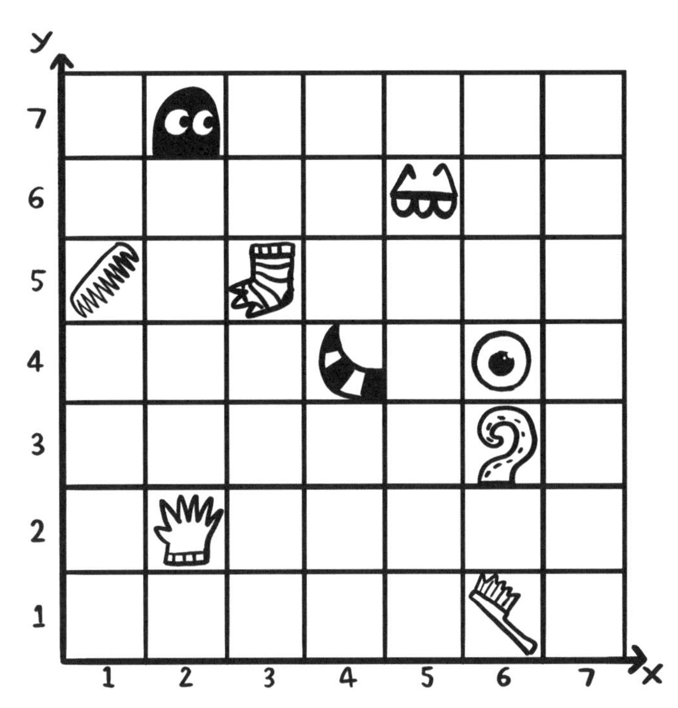

a) What are the coordinates of:

The comb?  ....

The glasses?  ....

The horn?  ....

b) Molly thinks the coordinates of the toothbrush  **are (1,6).**

Is she correct?

....

TOP TIP!

When using coordinates, you always read along the x axis before reading up or down the y axis. A common way to remember this is "Go along the corridor and up (or down) the stairs".

POSITION AND DIRECTION CONTINUED

You're doing great! Now, have a go at these questions.

1) The monsters are packing their bags.

Can you use the grid below and the compass on the right to answer the following questions?

Maurice

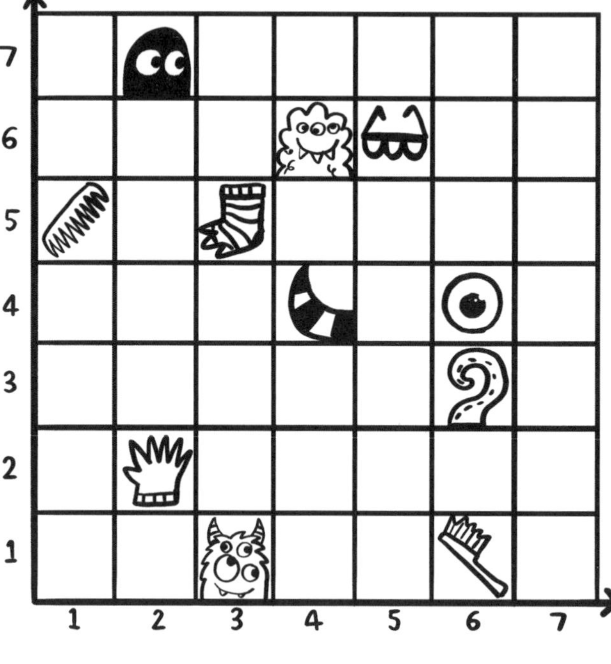

Molly

a) Maurice wants to get to his socks: 

How many squares and in what direction does he have to move?

....

b) Molly wants to get her gloves: 

How many squares and in what directions does she have to move?

....

2) The monsters want to take a kite on holiday with them.

a) Plot the following coordinates on the grid below to create a kite:

(5,1) (2,2) (2,4) (4,4) (5,1)

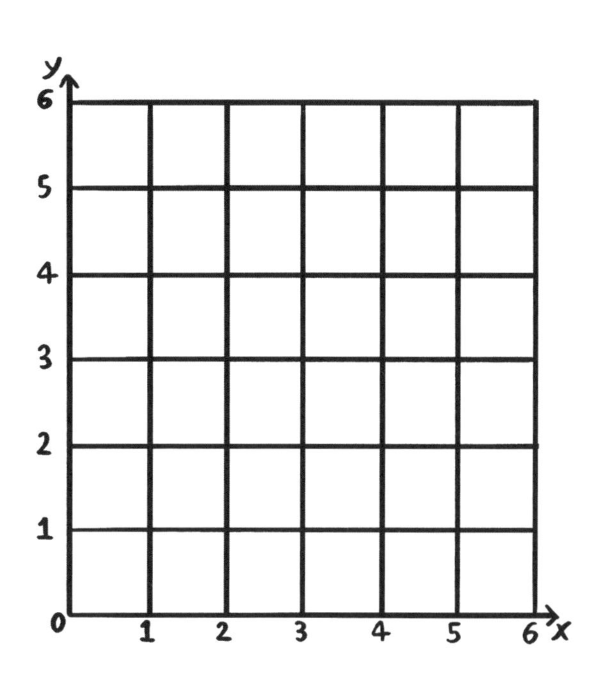

b) The kite translates 1 square left and 1 square up.

Draw the position of the kite now in the grid above.

3) Is the following statement true or false?

When you translate a shape you are making it larger.

....

HOORAY, FINISHED! ☐

STATISTICS

Can you use your knowledge of statistics to answer these questions?

1) Maurice and Molly are doing a survey of what superpowers their other monster friends have. Each monster can only have one superpower. Maurice and Molly have created a pictogram to show their results.

Key: 1 monster face = 4 monsters

Superpower	Number of Monsters
Invisibility	
Glow in the dark	
Super strength	
Flight	

a) What ability do the most amount of monsters possess?

....

b) How many more monsters can fly than have super strength?

....

c) What is the total number of monsters who can become invisible and those who can glow in the dark?

....

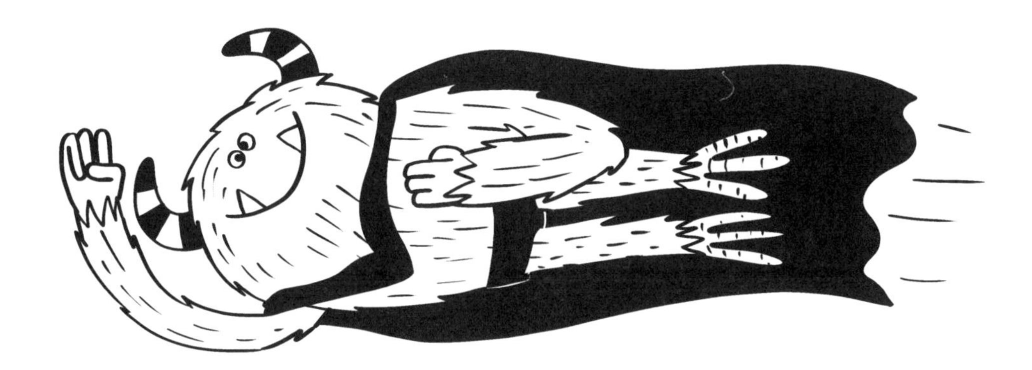

d) Some more monsters have been asked about their superpowers.

4 more can become invisible

2 more can fly

Can you add this information to the pictogram?

e) How many monsters, including the monsters asked in question **d)**, were surveyed in total?

....

TOP TIP!

When using pictograms, don't forget to check the key so that you know the quantity that each picture represents. With bar graphs (see page 50), you can always use a ruler to help you accurately read a value.

STATISTICS CONTINUED

You're doing great! Now, have a go at these questions.

1) **The monsters were asked about their favourite places to hide when playing hide-and-seek. Each monster only has one favourite place to hide. They have presented their results as a bar graph.**

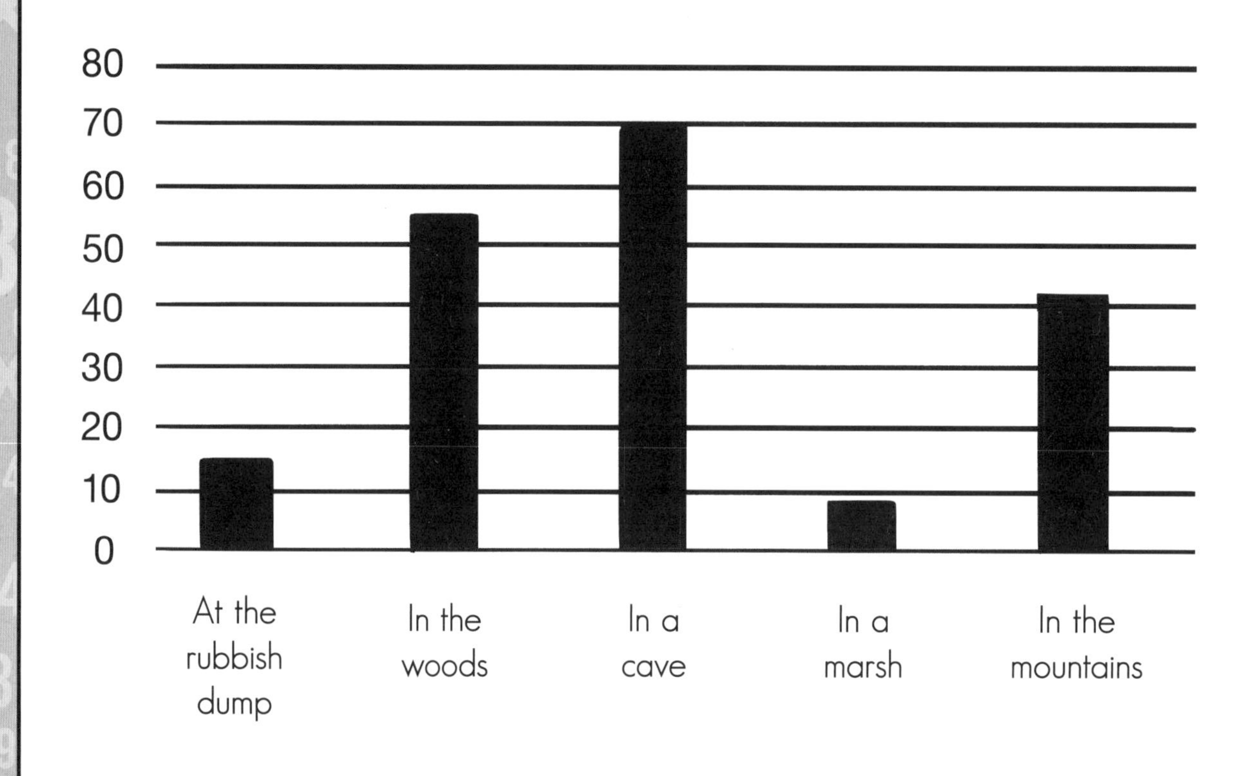

a) Which place is the least popular to hide?

....

b) Estimate how many monsters like to hide at the rubbish dump.

....

c) How many fewer monsters chose in the woods than in a cave?

....

d) Approximately how many monsters chose either the marsh or the mountains?

....

e) Which place did 70 monsters choose?

....

BONUS ACTIVITIES

1) The monsters have come across some Roman numerals.

Can you use the key to work out which numbers have been written?

I = 1
V = 5
X = 10
L = 50
C = 100
M = 1000

VII ....

XXX ....

CL ....

2) The monsters are investigating square numbers. When you square a number, you times it by itself. For example, $2^2 = 2 \times 2 = 4$

Can you calculate the next 3 square numbers? Use the grids to help you.

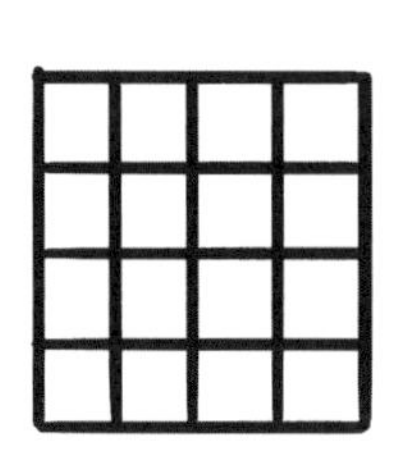

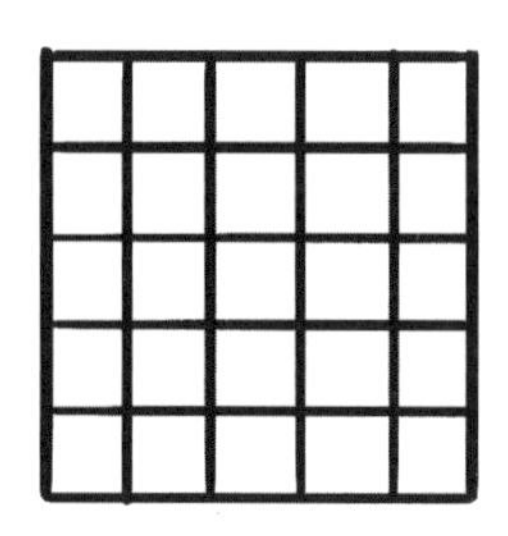

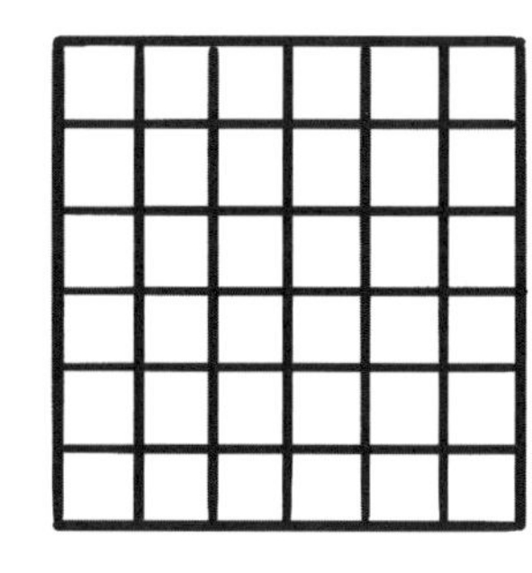

$2 \times 2 = 4$ $4 \times 4 =$ ☐ $5 \times 5 =$ ☐ $6 \times 6 =$ ☐

3) **Mo says that prime numbers are only divisible by themselves and 1. Mia has written some numbers that she thinks are prime.**

3, 5, 7, 9, 11, 13, 15

Is she correct?

....

4) **"Percent" means one part in every 100, so 1/100 = 1%.**

What percentage of each hundred square has been shaded grey?

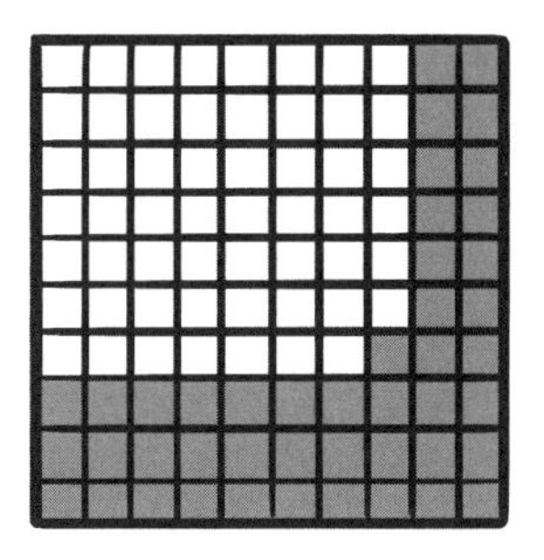

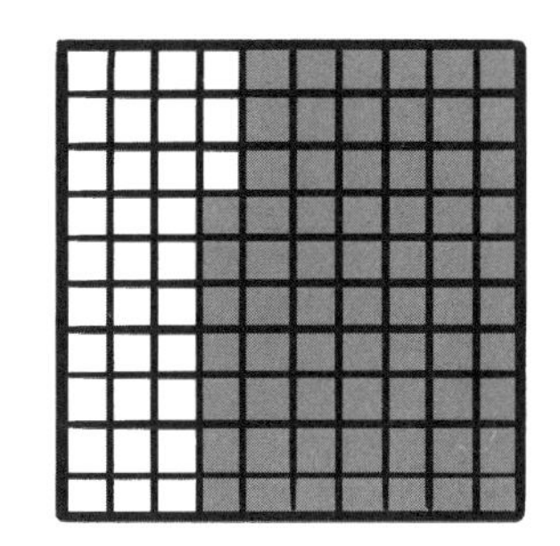

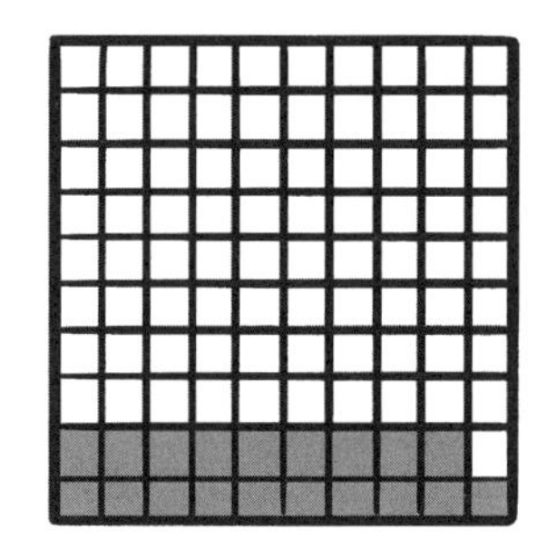

a) .... **b)** .... **c)** ....

5) **Can you solve these number problems?**

a) Which 5 different 1-digit numbers add together to make 15?

....

....

b) Which 3 different 1-digit numbers add up to 23?

....

....

HOORAY, FINISHED! ☐

ANSWERS

PAGES 4–5: NUMBER AND PLACE VALUE

1) a) 205
   b) 520
   c) True, because otherwise it would be a 2-digit number.

2) Maurice has counted up by 6 between 28 and 34.

3)

4) a) Molly has made 324 and 242.
   b)

5) a) 202
   b) Maurice is incorrect because that would only add 8. If Maurice put 112 into the machine, the next number would be 122.

PAGES 6–7: NUMBER AND PLACE VALUE CONTINUED

1) a) 30
   b) No, because $6 \times 12 = 72$.

2) The number Maurice is thinking of could be any of the following: 1402, 1412, 1422, 1432, 1442.

3) Molly is correct because when rounding to the nearest 100, if the tens digit is less than 5, the number will round down.

4) 5202, 4202, 3202, 2202

5) Maurice has added 10,000 instead of 1000. The next number should be 11,202.

PAGES 8–9: ADDITION AND SUBTRACTION

1) a) 332
   b) 221

2)
$$\begin{array}{r}215\\+\,143\\\hline 358\end{array}\qquad\begin{array}{r}458\\+\,339\\\hline 797\end{array}\qquad\begin{array}{r}596\\+\,424\\\hline 1020\end{array}$$

3) Maurice needs to exchange a ten so that the ones column becomes 16 - 7. The correct answer is 239.

4)

746	
432	314

923	
328	595

5)

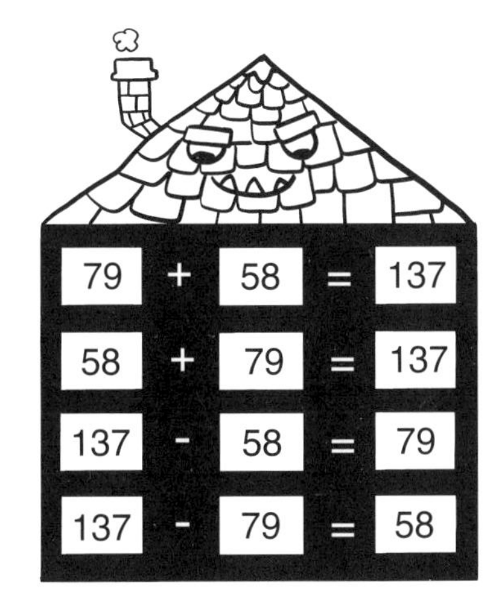

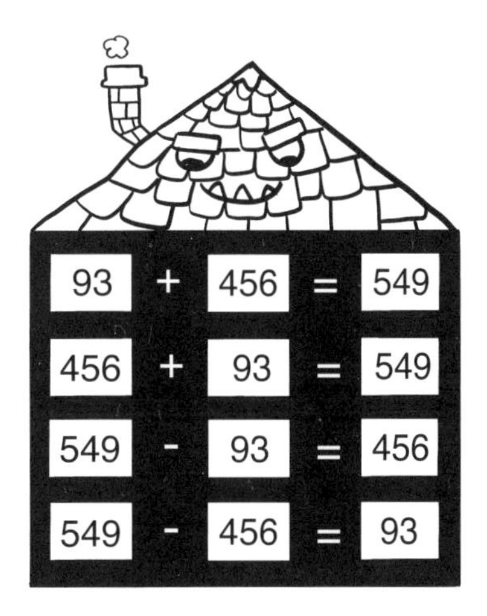

PAGES 10–11: ADDITION AND SUBTRACTION CONTINUED

1) No, because
80 + 70 = 150.

2) If I know that 60 + 40 = 100 then 600 + 400 = **1000**.
If I know that 200 - 130 = 70 then 2000 - **1300** = 700.

3)
```
 5472
-2381
 3091
```

4) Mo is more realistic because he has rounded 6943 correctly to 7000 whereas Mia has rounded down.

5) 137 monsters have scales.
734 + 329 = 1063 and
1200 - 1063 = 137

PAGES 12–13: MULTIPLICATION AND DIVISION

1) a) 3 × 4 = 12 4 × 5 = 20 2 × 4 = 8
4 × 3 = 12 5 × 4 = 20 4 × 2 = 8

b) 12 + 8 = 20 and 20 + 20 = 40

2) 7 × 3 = 21

3) (1 × 24)

(2 × 12)

(3 × 8)

(4 × 6)

4) 64 cm × 3 = 192 cm
31 cm × 4 = 124 cm
23 cm × 8 = 184 cm

5) No, the third monster has grown the most. Monster 1 has grown 128 cm, monster 2 has grown 93 cm and monster 3 has grown 161 cm.

ANSWERS

PAGES 14–15: MULTIPLICATION AND DIVISION CONTINUED

1) $240 \div 6 = 40$ $40 \times 60 = 2400$ $24{,}000 \div 6 = 4000$

2) Always true, for example, $9 \times 7 = 63$ and $5 \times 3 = 15$. You could use any example of two odd numbers multiplying together to make an odd number in your answer.

3) No, because the ones digit does not end in a 5 or a 0.

4) a) 1×48 2×24 3×16 4×12
b) 6×8

5) $9 \times 4 = 2 \times 6 \times 3$ is correct.
$3 \times 2 \times 7 = 8 \times 6$ is incorrect. $3 \times 2 \times 7 = 42$ and $8 \times 6 = 48$. To make them equal, you could rewrite 8×6 as 7×6.
$5 \times 12 = 5 \times 3 \times 2$ is incorrect. $5 \times 3 \times 2 = 30$ and $5 \times 12 = 60$. To make them equal, you could rewrite $5 \times 3 \times 2$ as $5 \times 6 \times 2$.

PAGES 16–17: FRACTIONS

1)
a) $\frac{1}{10}$ $\frac{2}{10}$ $\frac{3}{10}$ $\frac{4}{10}$ $\frac{5}{10}$ $\frac{6}{10}$ $\frac{7}{10}$ $\frac{8}{10}$ $\frac{9}{10}$ $\frac{10}{10}$

b) Yes, because they are equivalent which means the same; 5 is half of 10.

2) No, because you don't add the denominators together when adding fractions.
$\frac{4}{6} + \frac{3}{6} = \frac{7}{6}$. They have $\frac{7}{6}$ or $1\frac{1}{6}$ left.

3) False. The bigger the denominator, the smaller the part.
For example, $\frac{1}{4}$ is smaller than $\frac{1}{2}$.

4) a) $\frac{2}{8}$ or $\frac{1}{4}$

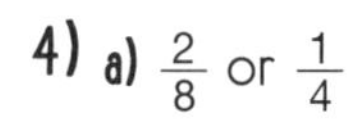

b) $\frac{3}{5}$

c) $\frac{2}{4}$ or $\frac{1}{2}$

5)

You could have shaded in any 1, 4 or 6 squares in each case.

PAGES 18-19: FRACTIONS CONTINUED

1) $\frac{11}{9}$

2) a) $\frac{2}{6}$ have wings.

b) $\frac{3}{9}$ have black horns.

c) $\frac{1}{3}$ have spots.

3) $\frac{1}{2} = \frac{4}{8}$ $\quad \frac{1}{4} = \frac{2}{8}$

$\frac{3}{4} = \frac{15}{20}$

4) a) $\frac{9}{10} - \frac{4}{10} = \frac{5}{10}$

b) $\frac{8}{10} - \frac{1}{10} = \frac{9}{10} - \frac{2}{10}$

c) $\frac{12}{10} - \frac{7}{10} = \frac{5}{10}$ equivalent to $\frac{1}{2}$

5) Your answer should show an object split into eight parts. 5 parts should be shaded in one colour and 3 parts should be shaded in another colour, to show that $\frac{3}{8} + \frac{5}{8} = 1$ whole.

PAGES 20-21: LENGTH

1) a) Molly's shadow (2 m) is the longest.
b) Maurice's shadow (91 cm) is the shortest.
c) The difference between Molly and Maurice's shadows is 109 cm or 1 m 9 cm.

2) a) The monster's tail is 17 cm.
b) 170 mm

3) 45 mm = 4.5 cm
4 m 50 cm = 450 cm
450 mm = 45 cm

4) Molly can jump 150 cm or 1 m 50 cm.

5) Molly can only use this method if the shape is regular (the sides are all the same length). She could use this method for the regular hexagon and regular pentagon, but not for the triangle or the rectangle.

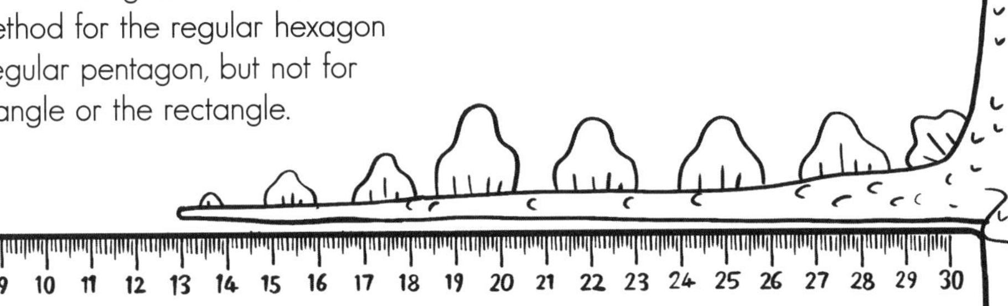

PAGES 22-23: LENGTH CONTINUED

1) To convince the monsters that 300 m is less than 3 km, your answer should show that 3 km is equivalent to 3000 m, so 300 m is less than 3 km.

2) Never true – when converting from mm to cm you divide by 10. If you included an example in your answer, give yourself an extra tick.

3) a) 29 cm
b) 56 cm

4) Maurice is incorrect – different shapes can still have the same area. By counting the squares inside the shapes, you can work out that they all have the same area.

5) a) 2000 m = 2 km
b) 5 km = 5000 m
c) 3600 m = 3 km and 600 m or 3.6 km

PAGES 24–25: MASS AND CAPACITY

1) Monster **b** weighs 37 kg, so it is the heaviest. Monster **a** weighs 35 kg and monster **c** weighs 36 kg.

2) 675 ml of squash is left.

3) Maurice is incorrect because 1 kg = 1000 g so $\frac{3}{4}$ of a kilogram is 750 g.

4)

To serve 2, divide the original amounts by 2:	To serve 8, multiply the original amounts by 2:
38 ml slug juice	152 ml slug juice
42 g snail shells	168 g snail shells
3 rotten eggs	12 rotten eggs
45 g beetles	180 g beetles

5) a) 450 ml
b) 650 ml
c) 100 ml

PAGES 26–27: MASS AND CAPACITY CONTINUED

1) A jug, a cup, a tablespoon, a teaspoon

2) An adult monster weighs 16 kg. To reach this answer, first work out that 4 kg × 8 = 32 kg. Then calculate that 32 kg ÷ 2 = 16 kg.

3) Maurice's bottle can hold 1650 ml.

4) 5 kg and 600 g > 560 g
1 L and 750 ml = 1750 ml
958 g < 9 kg and 580 g

5) Bag of flour = kg
Bottle of juice = L
Glass of water = ml
An apple = g

PAGES 28–29: MONEY

1) 20p 10p
20p 5p 5p

10p 10p 10p
10p 10p 5p 5p

10p 5p 5p 5p 5p
5p 5p 5p 5p 5p 5p

2) Although Molly has a five pound note, she does not have more money than Maurice. Molly's total is £5 and 70p and Maurice's total is £6 and 15p.

3)

£4 and 50p	
85p	£3 and 65p

£2 and 13p	
£1 and 14p	99p

4) Different combinations could include glow-in-the-dark slime and monster teeth, glow-in-the-dark slime and fake tail, monster teeth and fake tail, monster teeth and horn headband.

5) False: you need 10 because $10 \times 50p = £5$.

PAGES 30–31: MONEY CONTINUED

1) Yes, Maurice is correct. £10 + £2 + £1 = £13 and 20p + 20p + 2p = 42p. Your answer needs to show that £13 and 42p can be written using decimal notation as £13.42.

2) £7.01, £7.08, £7. 10, £7.18, £7.80, £7.81
£8.01, £8.07, £8.10, £8.17, £8.70, £8.71

3) £6.00 + 45p = £6.45. £10.00 - £6.45 = £3.55

4) £42 ÷ 6 = £7 and £42 - 7 = £35. Molly has £35 left.

5) Mia has two 50ps. Mo has a 50p, two 20ps and a 10p.

ANSWERS

PAGES 32-33: TELLING THE TIME

1) a) Molly = twenty-five past eight
   Mia = half past eight
   Mo = twenty past eight
   b) Mo goes to bed the earliest.

2) Molly is incorrect. Your answer should explain that 15 seconds is quicker than 17 seconds.

3) 15 seconds, 60 seconds, half an hour, 60 minutes

4) a) 9:08
   b) 7:22
   c) 10:35

5) Your explanation could show that you understand that there are 60 minutes in one hour. $180 = 60 \times 3$ so 180 minutes must be equivalent to 3 hours.

PAGES 34-35: TELLING THE TIME CONTINUED

1)

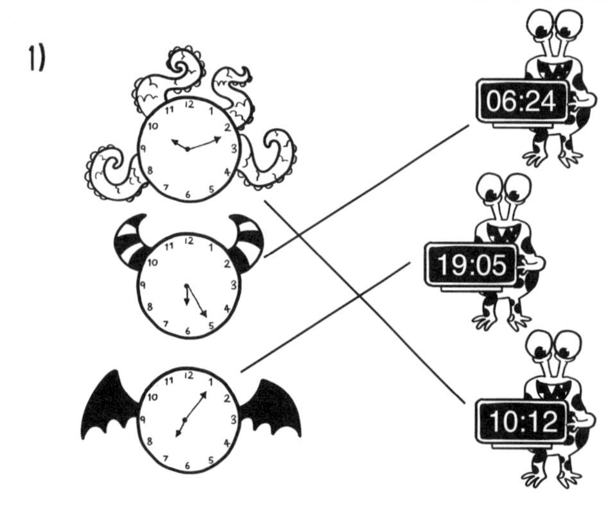

2) 14:20

3) 160 seconds

4) 00:02

5) Mia has confused the minute hand with the hour hand. The time on the clock is 10 minutes to 9 o'clock, or 8:50.

PAGES 36-37: TIME AND DATES

1) 1 minute < 100 seconds
   Number of days in January > Number of days in February
   30 days = Number of days in September

2) Mo's method is correct. You could use any multiple of 60 greater than 60 to convert minutes into hours. For example, 180, 240 or 300 divided by 60 (the number of minutes in an hour).

3) 12 o'clock in the afternoon is also known as **midday** or **noon**.
00:00 on a digital clock is also known as **midnight**.
4:30 am would be 4:30 in the **morning**.
4:30 pm would be 4:30 in the **afternoon**.

4) February, April, June, September and November have 30 days or less.

5) Maurice sleeps for 14 hours and sleeps the most per day. Molly sleeps for 12 hours and Mo sleeps for 13 hours and 15 minutes.

PAGES 38–39: TIME AND DATES CONTINUED

1) 9 am 2) 3 pm 3) a) 14:45 b) 19:20 c) 19:45

PAGES 40–41: GEOMETRY

1)

Horizontal

Perpendicular lines

Vertical

2) **b** and **d** are not parallel lines. Parallel lines are always straight lines with an equal distance between each other.

3) T shape (6), L shape (5), rectangle (4), heptagon (0)

4) Molly is thinking of a square-based pyramid.

5) Net **c** would not make a cube.

PAGES 42–43: GEOMETRY CONTINUED

1) Shapes **a** and **c** are triangles. Your explanation could say that a triangle is a 3-sided flat shape with straight lines. Shapes **b** and **d** do not have straight lines, so they are not triangles. If you used the word 'polygon' in your answer, give yourself an extra tick.

2) Sometimes. You could draw rectangles, squares, parallelograms or rhombuses to prove that some quadrilaterals do have 2 sets of parallel lines. Your answer should also explain that some quadrilaterals do not. For example, a kite or a trapezium.

ANSWERS

3)

4) a) Acute angle
b) Right angle
c) Obtuse angle

5)

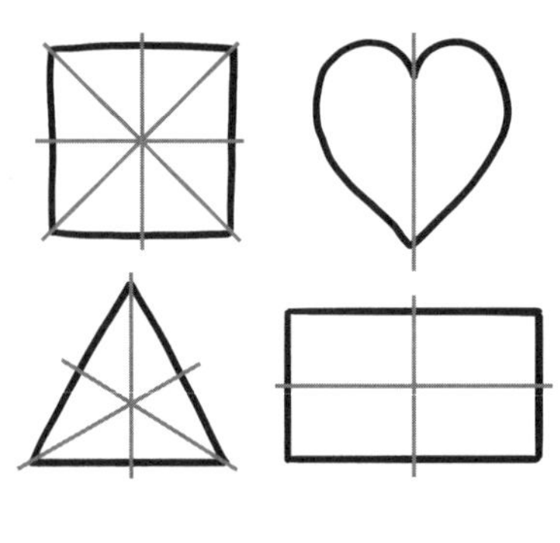

PAGES 44–45: POSITION AND DIRECTION

1) a) East
b) West

2) To prove that a complete turn is equivalent to 4 quarter turns, you could draw four right angles and connect them together to make a circle.

3) a) Comb = (1,5)
Glasses = (5,6)
Horn = (4,4)
b) Molly has read her coordinates incorrectly by reading the y axis then the x axis. The correct coordinates are (6,1).

PAGES 46–47: POSITION AND DIRECTION CONTINUED

1) a) Maurice needs to move 4 squares north to reach the socks.
b) Molly needs to move 2 squares west and then 4 squares south to reach the gloves.

2) a)

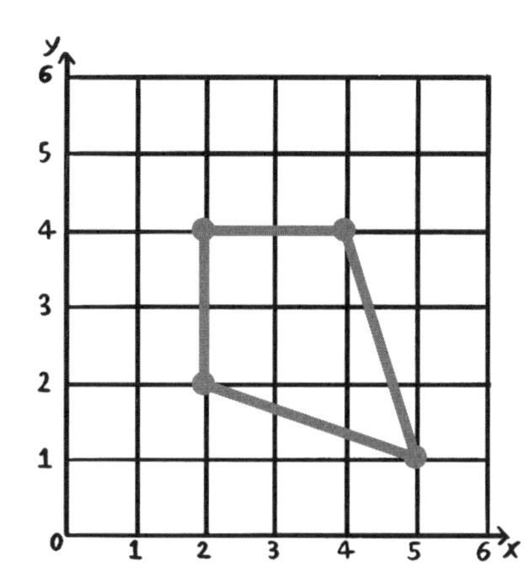

b)

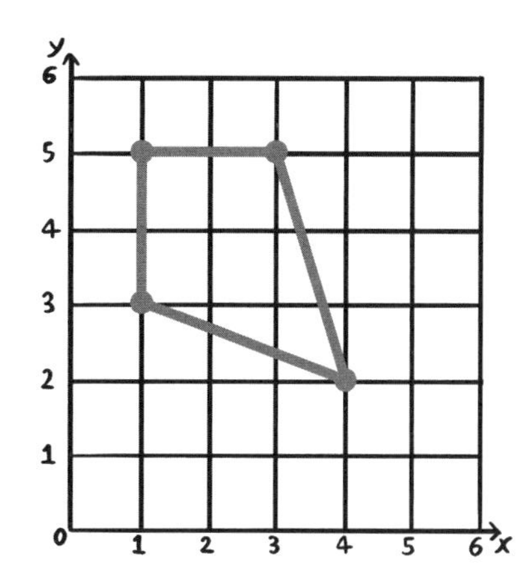

3) False. Translating a shape means that you are moving it, it should still remain the same size.

PAGES 48-49: STATISTICS

1) a) To glow in the dark
b) 2
c) 32 + 40 = 72
d) You should draw one more monster face for invisibility and half a monster face for flight.
e) 36 + 40 + 14 + 18 = 108

PAGES 50-51: STATISTICS CONTINUED

1) a) In a marsh
b) 14-16
c) 70 - 55 = 15
d) 9 + 42 = 51 but any answer in the range of 49-53 is fine.
e) In a cave

PAGES 52-53: BONUS ACTIVITIES

1) VII = 7 XXX = 30 CL = 150

2) $4 \times 4 = 16$ $5 \times 5 = 25$ $6 \times 6 = 36$

3) 9 is not a prime number because 3×3 is 9. 15 is not a prime number because $3 \times 5 = 15$. 3, 5, 7, 11 and 13 are prime numbers.

4) a) 45% (45/100)
b) 67% (67/100)
c) 19% (19/100)

5) a) 1 + 2 + 3 + 4 + 5 = 15
b) 6 + 8 + 9 = 23

GLOSSARY

Area
The amount of space inside the perimeter of a 2D shape.

Array
A set of pictures or numbers arranged in rows or columns to help with counting or calculating.

Bar graph
A graph that uses bars to show amounts.

Bar model
A diagram where bars are used to represent the known or unknown parts or whole.

Denominator
The bottom part of a fraction. The denominator shows how many equal parts an item is divided into.

Fact family
A group of maths equations that use the same numbers.

Function machine
A function machine takes a value (input) and applies a rule or formula, which then provides an output.

Multiplication sentence
An equation used to represent a multiplication. For example, $2 \times 2 = 4$ is a multiplication sentence.

Numerator
The top number of a fraction. The numerator shows how many parts you have out of a whole.

Parallel lines
Lines that are an equal distance apart, but never meet.

Perimeter
The distance around a 2D shape.

Pictogram
A chart that uses pictures or symbols to show information.

Quadrilateral
A 2D shape with four sides and four angles. For example, a square or rectangle.

Vertices
The points on a shape where two sides or edges meet.

First published in Great Britain in 2023 by Buster Books, an imprint of Michael O'Mara Books Limited,
9 Lion Yard, Tremadoc Road, London SW4 7NQ

W www.mombooks.com/buster  Buster Books  @BusterBooks  @buster_books

Clever Kids is a trade mark of Michael O'Mara Books Limited.

A CIP catalogue record for this book is available from the British Library.

ISBN: 978-1-78055-924-7

1 3 5 7 9 10 8 6 4 2

This book was printed in May 2023 by Leo Paper Products Ltd, Heshan Astros Printing Limited, Xuantan Temple Industrial Zone, Gulao Town, Heshan City, Guangdong Province, China